**Paperback PLUS
Teacher's Resources
Grade 5**

Table of Contents

2000 Impression

Copyright © 1997 by Houghton Mifflin Company
All rights reserved.

Designed and produced by PiperStudiosInc.
Illustration: PiperStudiosInc

Printed in U.S.A.
ISBN: 0-395-81926-1   6 7 8 9 10

Houghton Mifflin Company • Boston

Atlanta • Dallas • Geneva, Illinois • Palo Alto • Princeton

Literature in the Social Studies Classroom

Topical books—both fiction and nonfiction—can enliven the study of cultures, history, and geography in fresh, unexpected ways. Understanding the motives and actions of fictional characters helps young people develop empathy—a key ingredient in the evolution of self-knowledge and tolerance. Similarly, nonfiction books go into topics more deeply than is possible in a textbook. Carefully selected nonfiction proves that the truth makes a very good story.

When social studies instruction includes novels and historical fiction, students are far more receptive to learning. Why? Because the experiences of a well-drawn character create a context so memorable and powerful that suddenly the facts of history and geography are important to a young reader. In the same way, good nonfiction transcends mere information by opening up new views of people, events, and processes. Students who have read interesting books often want to learn more and are more likely to investigate further.

Good literature appeals to the heart and the intellect. It is an essential element in the social studies classroom.

Using the **Teacher's Resources** Booklet

Four pages of useful information and instructional material for each literature selection are featured in this *Teacher's Resources* booklet. The first page is an overview for the teacher, and the next three are blackline student activity masters.

The **Using the Book** page gives you a short synopsis of the book, outlines key themes, and suggests a way to introduce the book to your class.

Before Reading provides activities that help prepare the student for a successful reading experience. These activities can highlight prior knowledge, establish a context and purpose for reading, and encourage students to make predictions about the book.

Students complete the **Read and Respond** activities during or after reading. These activities focus on social studies themes and concepts and are designed to increase a student's understanding and enjoyment of the book.

The fourth page has two student activities. The **PLUS Activity** expands on the ideas and content of the PLUS pages, while the **Home Activity** encourages students to extend theme-related learning beyond the classroom.

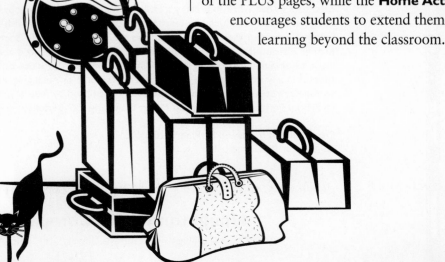

Paperback PLUS Planning Chart

Literature Selection	Summary	Social Studies Connections
The Sad Night: historical literature	This account of the Aztecs in Mexico includes the mythic origins of their empire and modern archaeological discoveries.	Legend vs. fact; Aztec culture; Old and New Worlds; Spanish exploration and conquest; Montezuma and Cortés; maps and images of artifacts
Pedro's Journal historical fiction	This novel about the first voyage of Columbus is written as dated entries in the journal of a cabin boy.	Conditions on Columbus's voyage; fears and superstitions of early explorers; primitive navigation and maps; world geography; ocean travel
Benjamin Franklin history	This classic biography of Ben Franklin tells his life story, his contributions, and accomplishments.	Colonial life; Franklin's contributions to education, publishing, technology, civic development, government, and international relations; the Revolution; the Constitution
Where Was Patrick Henry? biography	This entertaining biography of Patrick Henry tells about the life and times of an important leader, patriot, and statesman.	Colonial life in Virginia; Southern agricultural economy; importance of trade to the colonies; Revolution; post-Revolutionary War challenges
Sacajawea: Guide to Lewis and Clark biography	This book tells how a courageous Native American woman contributed to the success of the Lewis and Clark expedition.	Lewis and Clark; westward expansion; geography, wildlife, plants, natural resources, and native peoples of the Louisiana Territory
Harriet Tubman: Antislavery Activist biography	This thorough biography tells about Harriet Tubman's life of hardship and danger.	Slavery era in America; Underground Railroad; the failure of emancipation; key Civil War figures
Charley Skedaddle historical fiction	A 12-year-old New Yorker becomes a Union drummer boy in 1864 but "skedaddles" when faced with the horrors of his first battlefield.	Civil War army and civilian life; Underground Railroad; life in early Irish immigrant neighborhoods in New York and Virginia
The Cat Who Escaped From Steerage historical fiction	An immigrant family's trans-atlantic voyage to America in steerage.	Immigration at the turn of the 20th century; the Ellis Island experience; family bonds in immigrant families;
Song of the Trees realistic fiction	A neighboring white farmer cuts down trees on an African American's land.	Prejudice; Southern life during the Depression; motives of reformers like Dr. Martin Luther King, Jr.

Possible Answers for Read and Respond Activities

Page 3 *(Sad Night):* **1.** horror of the night, fierceness of the attackers, sadness at soldiers' deaths **2.** the thrill of defeating Spanish, the cleverness of the Aztec strategy, the defensive city design that helped them win, the sadness at losing so many friends, the justness of the Spanish defeat

Page 7 *(Pedro's Journal):* **1.** gentle, honest; careful to do his work well; upset about treatment of natives; faced storms at sea, unknown native people, and other dangers bravely **2.** Pedro might have wished there had been no natives on the island or that Columbus hadn't disregarded the rights of others or that he (Pedro) had never asked to steer the ship that night.

Page 11 *(Ben Franklin):* **1.** Poor Richard's Almanac **2.** started his own printing shop **3.** Franklin stove; lightning rod **4.** started a public library, a school, a police force, a hospital, a volunteer fire department; in charge of the post office **5.** delegate—to the King of England, to Declaration of Independence meetings, to Constitutional Convention; Ambassador to France **6.** Son, Brother, Husband, Father, Traveler, Scientist

Page 15 *(Where Was Patrick Henry):* **A. 1.** became a lawyer **2.** became a member of the House of Burgesses **3.** gave famous "liberty or death" speech **4.** became governor of Virginia **5.** made people demand a Bill of Rights **B.** wanted the states to have more rights **C.** a Bill of Rights

Page 19 *(Sacajawea):* **1.** not afraid to go on the expedition; overcame her fear to become a translator in council meetings **2.** used her knowledge to find food and safe passage **3.** carried Pompey on the whole journey **4.** gave up her bead belt for the good of the expedition **5.** never gave up in spite of sickness and hard conditions. **6.** Able to help explorers communicate with native peoples they met. Sacajawea knew the way, how to travel in rough country, and how to find food.

Page 23 *(Harriet Tubman):* **1.** kept her dignity; learned to work hard **2.** used her intelligence to avoid capture **3.** showed great courage; worked tirelessly **4.** did all she could to get supplies; started school for ex-slaves **5.** led a successful raid into enemy territory **6.** rescued her parents **7.** rescued friends **8.** helped others in her town

Page 27 *(Charley Skedaddle)* Students could write about Charley's escape from the army; his capture and release by the Confederates; how he learned he was not a coward; how he learned that war was horrible.

Page 31 *(The Cat Who Escaped Steerage)* The story leaves plenty of room for creative responses as students consider the action through the eyes of various characters.

Page 35 *(Song of the Trees)* **1.** Mr. Anderson decided how many trees he could cut for $65, not Big Ma, and he threatened her son with "an accident." **2.** Because the sheriff was a white man, they probably thought he would have agreed with Mr. Anderson no matter what. **3.** He thought being white made him able to do whatever he wanted to. **4.** Papa had worked hard for their own land and for their self-respect and wouldn't let Mr. Anderson harm either of these.

The Sad Night: The Story of an Aztec Victory and a Spanish Loss
written and illustrated by Sally Schofer Mathews

About the Book

This is the story of the Aztecs in Mexico. After tracing the mythic origins of the Aztec Empire, the book gives historical facts, including the arrival of the Spanish, a great battle in the year 1519, and modern archaeological discoveries in what is now Mexico City.

Social Studies Links

This book begins with legends and then tells known facts. The illustrations are based on the remaining Aztec fold-out books, or codices, most of which were destroyed by the Spanish. The book shows the relationship of the Old World to the New World. The text touches on cultural elements such as art, religion, and government; it can prompt a discussion of Spanish exploration and conquest. Important historical figures like Montezuma and Cortés are introduced. Illustrations include maps and images of artifacts.

Getting Students Started

On a world map, point out Mexico and Spain. Explain that before Spanish conquistadors came across the ocean looking for land and gold, various Native American groups ruled the area now called Mexico. The most successful—and brutal—of these were the Aztecs. Explain that this book is an introduction to both the Aztecs and the Spanish conquerors who came from the Old World. *The Sad Night* is ideal for in-class independent reading.

PLUS and Beyond

The PLUS pages focus on the first-person account of Bernal Díaz del Castillo, a young man who entered Tenochtitlán with Hernando Cortés in 1519. Bernal Díaz presents detailed descriptions of the city and clearly admires the culture and art of the Aztecs. The realistic illustrations of the ancient city and the photographs of actual artifacts and modern Mexico City are a good counterpoint to the stylized illustrations of *The Sad Night*.

Name _____ Date _____

 The Sad Night

What Makes Up a Culture?

Long before the Aztecs developed an empire, they were just one of many small
tribes in a tropical region, each with its own culture.

Look at the list below. These are some of the elements that make up a culture.
These elements can affect the survival of a civilization.

Think of one or two ways that each of these different elements might be important
to the survival and success of an ancient people.

cultural element	how it might be important to a group's success
religion	
art	
architecture	
agriculture	
tools	
weapons	
transportation	
education	
medicine	

After reading *The Sad Night,* you may want to think about the Spanish as if they
were a just another tribe. How did they use these same cultural elements?

Name _____   Date _____

One Event, Two Views

Two stories about the very same event can be completely different. How
the event is described depends on the point of view of the reporter.

1. **Think about a Spanish survivor of The Sad Night.**
    What would he write in a journal entry for that event?

    _____

    _____

    _____

    _____

    _____

    _____

    _____

    _____

2. **Think about being an Aztec warrior after the same battle. Write a short**
    journal entry from the Aztec point of view.

    _____

    _____

    _____

    _____

    _____

    _____

    _____

PLUS Activity

Searching for Tenochtitlán

On the PLUS pages you can see an artist's picture of what Tenochtitlán looked like in 1519.

Do some research in your school or public library about Tenochtitlán. How have people learned that Tenochtitlán looked like that? Can you find other drawings or paintings showing how the ancient city may have looked?

After you have done some research, write a short report—no longer than two paragraphs— that tells how modern people have learned about Tenochtitlán. At the end of your report, list the research sources you used.

 The Sad Night

Home Activity

Past, Present, Future

Near the end of *The Sad Night*, the author tells about the Aztec calendar.

If you were in charge of making up a new calendar, what would it look like? Would it have 12 months and 365 days like ours, or would it break time up into some other units? What would you name the different units of time? Would you decorate your calendar with any special symbols?

After you have made your calendar, write a short explanation of how it works. Take your calendar to school to share with your classmates.

Pedro's Journal
by Pam Conrad, illustrated by Peter Koeppen

About the Book

This is historical fiction about the first voyage of Columbus. It is written as dated entries in the journal of a cabin boy whose name was in the actual ship's roster. Pedro records his observations of the voyage, the landfall, the treatment of the Taino people, and the return voyage to Spain.

Social Studies Links

The historical significance of Columbus's voyages cannot be overemphasized. Readers will empathize with the difficulties of early sea voyages, Pedro's fears and superstitions, inadequate navigation and maps, and how close Columbus came to turning back. The many illustrations clarify details about the ships and key moments in the story. The study of world geography, ocean travel, and map skills are logical extensions of this book.

Getting Students Started

To set the stage for this book, help students to empathize with the common seamen and Pedro to understand their deep fears. Discuss with them how little was known about the world in 1491. If possible, go to the library to find a picture of a pre-Columbian map and show it to students, comparing it with a modern world map. Ask students why most people believed then that the world was flat and that there were huge monsters in the sea. Help them see that as Pedro says good-bye to his mother, he is not setting off on an ordinary trip. Have students read *Pedro's Journal* independently.

PLUS and Beyond

The PLUS pages have two nonfiction features. One tells about the 500-year anniversary voyage of the *Niña,* the *Pinta,* and the *Santa Maria.* The three ships were replicas of the originals. In 1992 they sailed the same course as the original ships had. Also in the PLUS pages is a description of the hardships faced by sailors of that era. Both of these features are starting points for further research and study.

Name _____ Date _____

 Pedro's Journal

Historical Fiction: Mixing Facts and Nonfacts

Pedro's Journal is historical fiction. It is based on factual events, but nonfacts have been added to help tell an interesting story. Writers of historical fiction do a lot of research so that their nonfacts stay close to what may have really happened.

Think about a boy who once took a bus trip west from Chicago, Illinois. Here are the facts we know:

> Name: Reynold Carter
>
> Age: ten years old
>
> Other facts: tall for his age; Chicago Cubs fan; wore black high-top basketball shoes every day; owned a camera; loved to take pictures; left Chicago on a bus with his 19-year-old sister Annette on April 3, 1979; arrived in Los Angeles, California, on April 5, 1979

Use this information as your only known facts and write some historical fiction about Reynold. You could write a short journal entry as if Reynold were telling about something that happened on his bus ride. You could include nonfactual conversations, or you could tell about something as if his sister or the bus driver were talking. Because this is historical fiction, you may invent nonfactual details that make sense within the framework of the facts you know.

_____

_____

_____

_____

_____

As you read *Pedro's Journal,* be aware of what is factual information and what is nonfactual.

Name _____   Date _____

Looking Through Pedro's Eyes

1. During the long voyage, we get to know Pedro de Salceda. How would you
   describe him? Think in terms of qualities. Is he brave or fearful; generous
   or selfish; kind or mean, and so on? Write a short character sketch of
   Pedro and give examples to back up your description.

   _____

   _____

   _____

   _____

   _____

   _____

2. Once an event happens, it is history, and no one can go back in
   time and change it—but sometimes we might wish we could.
   Based on what you learned about Pedro, if he were able
   to change history just by rewriting a part of his
   journal, what might he wish he could change? Pick
   a part of his journal Pedro might want to change
   the most, and rewrite it for him.

   _____

   _____

   _____

   _____

   _____

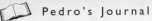
PLUS Activity

On Board the <u>Santa Maria</u>

You can read in the PLUS pages about a sailor's daily life in Columbus's day. Pedro also tells a lot about life on board his ship.

Think about what it was like to be a sailor. Then write one paragraph that tells what you might like about it and one paragraph about what you would not like. You could also include illustrations to support your statements.

✂ -

 📖 Pedro's Journal

Home Activity

One Day, One Journal Entry

Think of a trip that you or someone in your family has taken. Pick one day from that trip, and make a list of the main events in the order they happened. Then write a journal entry as if you are at the end of that day and sitting down to write about what has happened. Be sure to include dates, names, and places as needed.

Ben Franklin
by Ingri & Edgar Parin D'Aulaire

About the Book

This is a classic children's biography of Ben Franklin. His life story is told, and his contributions and accomplishments are set into the context of Colonial America and the founding of the nation.

Social Studies Links

Words and pictures in this book give a clear sense of Colonial life. In his day, Franklin was at the forefront of education, publishing, technology, civic development, government, and international relations. There is hardly an aspect of early American life that cannot be explored by starting with the life and experiences of Benjamin Franklin.

Getting Students Started

Most students will know the name of Benjamin Franklin. Some may know that his face appears on the one hundred dollar bill. But few will realize how much Franklin did in his life. Ask students how many have parents or grandparents who wear bifocal glasses. Tell them Ben invented them. Ask how many have ever felt the heat from a metal wood stove. Tell them Ben invented it. Ask if anyone has ever seen a lightning rod on the top of barn, a church, or a tower. Tell them Ben invented that, too. The class should read this book independently.

PLUS and Beyond

The PLUS pages show period paintings and illustrations of some of Franklin's more famous inventions. The pages also trace his travels and influence on the colonies and the young nation. It's hard to make too much of the accomplishments of this writer/inventor/patriot/statesman.

Name _____ Date _____

 Ben Franklin

Living in Colonial America

Benjamin Franklin was born in Boston in 1706. Many things changed during Ben's lifetime, and he was at the center of those changes. Before you read about Ben Franklin's life, think about what you already know or have read about those days in America. Then write answers to the questions below, and briefly explain your answers.

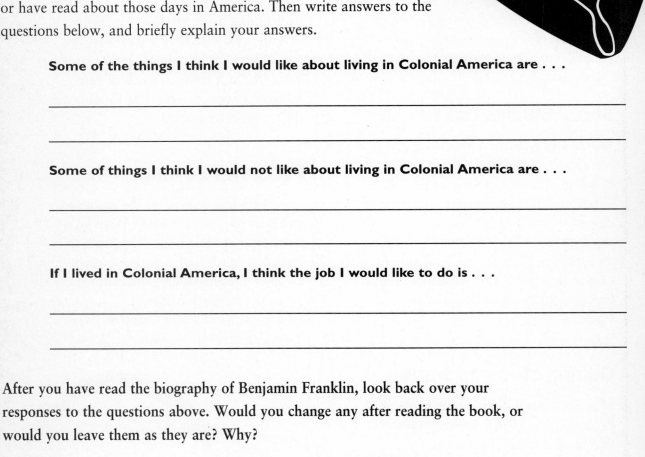

Some of the things I think I would like about living in Colonial America are . . .

_____

_____

Some of things I think I would not like about living in Colonial America are . . .

_____

_____

If I lived in Colonial America, I think the job I would like to do is . . .

_____

_____

After you have read the biography of Benjamin Franklin, look back over your responses to the questions above. Would you change any after reading the book, or would you leave them as they are? Why?

_____

_____

Name _____ Date _____

A Life of Accomplishments

Ben Franklin did many different things during his life. As you read, keep track of his accomplishments by making notes under the headings on the chart below.

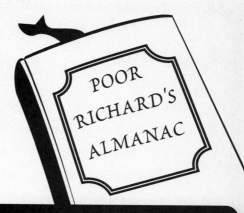

POOR RICHARD'S ALMANAC

Ben Franklin's Accomplishments				
1. Writer	2. Printer	3. Inventor	4. Citizen	5. Statesman

6. After reading the book, what other headings could you add to the chart?

PLUS Activity
Enduring Inventions

Make a poster or write a one-page report about one of Ben Franklin's inventions that is still used today. Explain how, when, where, and why it was invented. You may need to use an encyclopedia or other reference sources. If the invention has changed during the years, tell how and why.

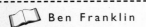

Home Activity
Poor Richard Then and Now

Pick one of the sayings from *Poor Richard's Almanac.* Make a poster that includes the original saying and then a modern translation of the saying. Have your illustrations show what the saying means today. You can use pictures cut from magazines or newspapers or make your own pictures. Bring your finished poster to school to show your classmates.

Where Was Patrick Henry on the 29th of May?
by Jean Fritz
illustrated by Margot Tomes

About the Book

This entertaining biography of Patrick Henry tells about the life and times of an important pre-Revolutionary leader, patriot, and statesman.

Social Studies Links

The anecdotal style of this biography takes students into the heart of colonial life in Virginia. They learn about the pace of life, the agricultural economy and its early reliance on slavery, the importance of trade to the colonies, the gradual assertion of British control, and the urge for self-government that led to the Revolution. Reading about Patrick Henry's five terms as governor of Virginia and of his opposition to the Constitution, students learn that winning the War of Independence was not the end of young America's challenges.

Getting Students Started

Remind your students that colonists had lived in Virginia for more than 150 years before the Revolution. They braved great dangers and hardships to build up their properties and their trade. When the English king began to take money from them with unfair taxes, the colonists didn't like it—and Patrick Henry was one of the first Virginians to stand up in public and say so. The class should read this biography independently.

PLUS and Beyond

The PLUS pages include a map that shows the enormous size of the Virginia colony. There is also a gallery of other important early Americans who, like Patrick Henry, made famous statements. Any of these people could be researched further during study of the Revolutionary period.

Name _____ Date _____

 Where was Patrick Henry on the 29th of May?

What's a Patriot?

Think about what it means to be a patriot. It may help to look up the words *patriot, patriotic,* and *patriotism* in a dictionary. Think about what you know of American history and about the men and women that Americans call patriots. In your own words, answer the questions below.

What are some of the important qualities a patriot usually has?

_____

_____

What famous Americans can you think of who can be called patriots?

_____

_____

Pick one of the patriots you listed and tell what you know about his or her accomplishments.

_____

_____

Each nation on earth has its own patriots. Can you think of a man or woman who is a patriot in a country other than the United States?

_____

_____

As you read *Where Was Patrick Henry on the 29th of May*, notice the things Patrick Henry said and did that made him an American patriot.

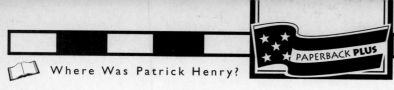

Name _____   Date _____

Deciding What's Important

A. After reading about Patrick Henry's life, decide what you think were the five most important events or accomplishments in his life. List each event or accomplishment in the table below, and write one or two sentences that tell why you think it was important.

Event or accomplishment	Why it was important?
1.	
2.	
3.	
4.	
5.	

B. Why was Patrick Henry against the new United States Constitution?

_____

_____

_____

C. What was added to it that made him feel better about it?

_____

_____

PLUS Activity
Famous Early Americans

Choose one of the people who is quoted in the PLUS pages near the end of the book. Do some research to learn more about this person, using encyclopedias or other reference sources. Then write a ten-sentence report telling why this person was important in early American history.

Home Activity
Picturing an Idea

Patrick Henry's most famous statement is "Give me liberty, or give me death!"

Make a poster that illustrates what the word *liberty* means to you. You may want to draw or paint your own images, or you could make a collage from pictures cut from magazines and newspapers.

Sacajawea: Guide to Lewis and Clark
by Della Rowland
illustrated by Richard Leonard

About the Book

Assembled from the known facts about Sacajawea, this book tells how a courageous Native American woman contributed to the success of the Lewis and Clark expedition. The publishers state, "No part of this biography has been fictionalized."

Social Studies Links

The Lewis and Clark expedition was an important step in the growth of the United States. This journey greatly increased knowledge about the geography, wildlife, plants, natural resources, and native peoples of the Louisiana Territory. Students gain empathy for the hardships endured by early travelers and for the Native Americans whom the explorers encountered.

Getting Students Started

Review facts from the text about the Louisiana Purchase, and point out the territory on a map. Locate the place on the Missouri River where the Corps of Discovery built Fort Mandan. This fort was where Lewis and Clark hired Sacajawea to be the explorers' interpreter. Not only did she journey to the Pacific with the men, but she carried her newborn baby the whole way! The students should read the book independently.

PLUS and Beyond

The PLUS section provides some additional background information about Sacajawea's people, the Shoshoni. There is also a map that clearly outlines the route taken by the expedition from St. Louis to the Pacific. Key events of the trip west and the return journey are located on the map, making it a useful tool for students to use while reading.

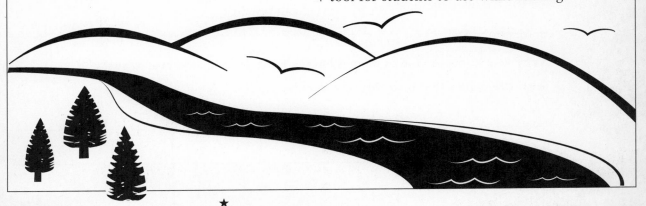

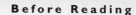
Name _____ Date _____

 Sacajawea: Guide to Lewis and Clark

Setting the Scene

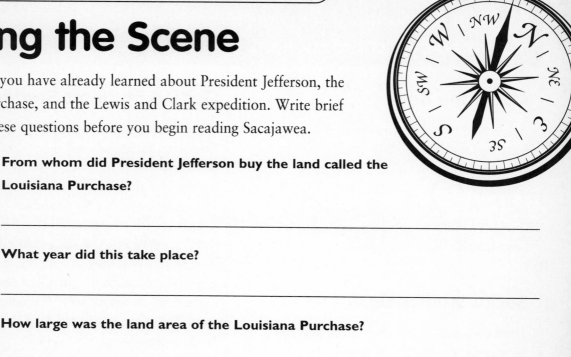

Review what you have already learned about President Jefferson, the Louisiana Purchase, and the Lewis and Clark expedition. Write brief answers to these questions before you begin reading Sacajawea.

From whom did President Jefferson buy the land called the Louisiana Purchase?

_____

What year did this take place?

_____

How large was the land area of the Louisiana Purchase?

_____

How far westward did the Purchase extend the territory of the United States?

_____

_____

Why did Jefferson hope the Corps of Discovery would discover a river to the Pacific Ocean?

_____

_____

Why was it important to have a Native American interpreter travel with the expedition into this new territory?

_____

_____

Name _____   Date _____

The Qualities of an Explorer

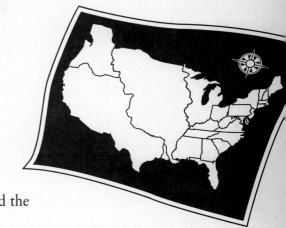

Sacajawea had a number of personal qualities and abilities that
made her able to travel with the Lewis and Clark expedition
and to help the explorers reach their goal. As you read the
book, make note of situations or examples where Sacajawea used the
qualities or abilities listed below.

Quality	Examples of the quality or ability in action
1. courage	
2. intelligence	
3. strength	
4. unselfishness	
5. persistence	

6.   **What were the special circumstances of Sacajawea's life history that
     helped make her a valuable member of the expedition?**

_____

_____

_____

_____

_____

PLUS Activity

If They Went Today

In 1803 Sacajawea and the Corps of Discovery traveled west through uncharted territory.

Using a modern map of the United States, begin at St. Louis and list in order all the states that the expedition would pass through if they made the same westward trip today.

Hint: Use the rivers and the trail shown on the map in the PLUS section to find the expedition's path on the modern map.

 Sacajawea

Home Activity

Fictionalizing a Fact

Pick a real event or incident from Sacajawea's experience with the Corps of Discovery. Think about how Sacajawea might have described this experience herself.

Write a paragraph about the experience as if you were Sacajawea telling what happened. Use your known facts carefully so that what you write sounds as real as possible.

PAPERBACK PLUS

Harriet Tubman: Antislavery Activist
by M. W. Taylor

About the Book

This thorough biography tells about Harriet Tubman's life of hardship, danger, and unselfish labor and makes plain why she is regarded as a hero.

Social Studies Links

Students learn of the slavery era in America, the resistance of slaves and abolitionists, the background of the Civil War, the political battles over new states entering the Union, the Underground Railroad, the abolition movement, and the failure of emancipation to provide true civil rights for African Americans. The book also teaches about key historical figures such as Frederick Douglass, John Brown, and Susan B. Anthony and explains the important role of African Americans in the Union victory.

Getting Students Started

Ask students to review the experiences of enslaved African Americans. Escape was their dream. Harriet Tubman did not just dream. Hers was a life of action. Some readers will find this book challenging. Teachers may want to assign the book in 20-page sections on successive nights to allow for class discussion and follow-up. It may be helpful to read selected passages aloud in class to highlight key events.

PLUS and Beyond

The PLUS pages contain original source materials from the age of American slavery: the song "Swing Low, Sweet Chariot" and an excerpt from Frederick Douglass's 1845 autobiography. You may want to read the first-person statement by Frederick Douglass aloud with your students before they begin reading Harriet Tubman's story. Douglass describes powerful emotions, and understanding these emotions may help students identify with the challenges that Harriet Tubman and so many other African Americans faced during this period.

Name _____ Date _____

 Harriet Tubman: Antislavery Activist

A Way To Serve Others

Read the foreword to *Harriet Tubman*. It was written by
Coretta Scott King, widow of Dr. Martin Luther King, Jr.
In the foreword she says that her husband, like Harriet
Tubman and other great leaders, found ". . . a way to serve
others, instead of living only for themselves."

Think of some other people who fit into this category of ". . . not
living only for themselves." They could be people you have actually
met or people you have learned about. Write their names in the spaces below, and
tell one or two things they did to help others.

People ". . . not living only for themselves."

What they did ". . . to serve others."

As you read about Harriet Tubman, notice the many ways she served others.

Name _____ Date _____

Actions Make a Life

Harriet Tubman is remembered more for what she did than what she said. During her life she played many different roles, did many different kinds of work, and knew many different kinds of people.

Read through the list of roles below. As you read *Harriet Tubman,* write down one or more important things she did or accomplished in each role.

	Event or accomplishment
1. as a slave	
2. as a runaway	
3. as a "Conductor"	
4. as a nurse or caregiver	
5. as soldier	
6. as a daughter	
7. as a friend	
8. as a neighbor	

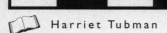

PAPERBACK PLUS

PLUS Activity

What's in a Song?

Read through the words of "Swing Low, Sweet Chariot" in the PLUS pages. Briefly tell why you think this particular spiritual was Harriet Tubman's favorite song. Refer to events or circumstances in her life to support your ideas.

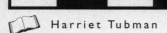

Home Activity

A Different Kind of "Wanted" Poster

Harriet Tubman was treated like a criminal in the old South. "Wanted" posters that promised a large reward for her capture were posted.

What if "Wanted" posters were made so people could find someone who was doing many good things? Instead of a "Wanted" poster, we might have an "Honored" poster. What would Harriet Tubman's "Honored" poster be like?

Make a poster that tells about the good things that Harriet Tubman should be honored for.

Charley Skedaddle
by Patricia Beatty

About the Book

Charley Skedaddle is historical fiction about a 12-year-old New Yorker who becomes a Union drummer boy in 1864 but "skedaddles" when faced with the horrors of his first battlefield. Hiding out in the mountains of western Virginia, he slowly recovers his self-respect.

Social Studies Links

Rich with facts about life in New York City, in the Union army, and in the Virginia hill country during the Civil War, this book recreates the texture and tone of an era. It also includes information about the Underground Railroad and about life in Irish immigrant neighborhoods in New York.

Getting Students Started

Tell students that boys as young as ten years old served as drummers in both the Union and Confederate armies during the Civil War. Hundreds were killed, and many thousands were wounded. In the days before walkie-talkies, drummers provided communication on smoky or tree-covered battlefields. This fictional story is based on historical facts. Students should read the novel independently.

PLUS and Beyond

The PLUS pages present a Civil War timeline and capsule biographies of Ulysses S. Grant and Robert E. Lee. Before reading *Charley Skedaddle*, you may want to have your class read about Grant and Lee and become familiar with the major events on the timeline. Reading about these two generals will help students understand the factual framework within which the author is creating her fictional account.

Name _____ Date _____

 Charley Skedaddle

Thinking Like a Writer of Historical Fiction

Think about being a writer of historical fiction: Your topic is the Civil War. You must make a reader feel as if he or she is really there. To do this, you must supply realistic details. You must describe people, places, objects, and events so they will seem real to the reader.

Look at the list of persons, places, objects, and events in the left-hand column below. Using what you may already know about the Civil War, write down details that could be used by a writer to make historical fiction more believable. Write down one or two details for each setting.

As you read *Charley Skedaddle*, notice how Patricia Beatty uses details to help you get involved with the story.

	Setting: An Army Camp	Setting: A Battlefield
scenery		
sounds		
smells		
food		
weapons		
clothes		
soldiers		
animals		

Name _____ Date _____

What Charley Thought About

You can look in Chapter 5 of the book and see what Charley wrote to his sister before he went into battle. He couldn't say much about where he was or what he had been doing. Later, he was too frightened and ashamed to write to her.

Near the end of the book, Charley decides to head off on his own again. Think about all the things Charley experienced and the ways he had changed since the time he wrote that first letter to Noreen. Speaking as if you were Charley near the end of the book, write a letter to Noreen on the lines below.

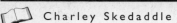

PLUS Activity

Putting Charley on the Timeline

On a sheet of $8\frac{1}{2}$ by 11 inch paper turned sideways, make a timeline like the one in the PLUS pages. Above the line, copy in the factual dates and events listed on the timeline. Below the line, add the major events from Charley's Civil War experience. The novel refers to many actual events and battles. These references will help you find actual dates to match up with Charley's fictional story.

✂ -

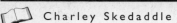 Charley Skedaddle

Home Activity

Choosing Something Important

Tell someone at home the story of Charley Skedaddle. Ask that person to help you pick a scene, an event, or an object that is important to the story. Then, using markers, crayons, paper collage, or any other type of art materials you like, make a poster to illustrate what you have chosen. On the same paper as your illustration, write a short explanation of why what you chose is important.

The Cat Who Escaped from Steerage
by Evelyn Wilde Mayerson

About the Book

This realistic fiction recounts an immigrant family's transatlantic voyage to America in steerage, the least costly passage. The family—a father, mother, daughter, son, and some other relatives—are Polish Jews who are looking for a better life in America.

Social Studies Links

This story will help students identify with the millions of European immigrants who crossed the Atlantic and then faced the inspectors at Ellis Island. In this richly human story, a family faces its difficulties with determination, intelligence, humor, and love. Students will learn about the poverty, hopes, and dreams that brought families to America.

Getting Students Started

It's good to remind students that Native Americans are the only Americans whose ancestors are not immigrants. Millions of immigrants came to the United States from Europe between 1892 and 1914, and most of them passed through Ellis Island in New York harbor. Other millions of immigrants came from Asia to Hawaii and the West Coast and from Latin America to Florida and California. Students should read *The Cat Who Escaped from Steerage* independently.

PLUS and Beyond

The PLUS pages include documentary photographs of Ellis Island, a map of New York harbor, and a first-person narrative by an immigrant who came to America from Italy in 1903. This material will help students to understand that each immigrant has his or her own personal history—a rich story about the hope for a better life in this country.

Name _____ Date _____

 The Cat Who Escaped from Steerage

Traveling in Steerage

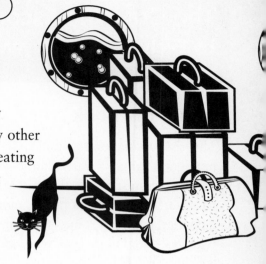

Traveling in steerage meant riding several levels down from any sunshine or fresh air and being crowded into a space with many other families for several weeks. It meant sleeping on narrow bunks, eating poor food, and trying to survive in bad sanitary conditions. But still immigrants came to America by the millions.

Think about traveling in steerage with a poor family across the Atlantic Ocean, and answer the questions below as best you can.

If you could bring along one or two things of your own, what might they be? Why?

_____

_____

There would probably be other children your age on board. What kinds of things could you do together that might be fun?

_____

_____

What do you think might be the worst part about traveling in steerage?

_____

_____

If you asked the father of the poor family to tell why he wanted to get to America, what might his answer be?

_____

Name _____ Date _____

A Hard Voyage, But Memorable

For the characters in *The Cat Who Escaped from Steerage*, the trip to America was hard, but it was not all bad. Things happened that were also interesting, memorable, and even funny.

For each of the characters below, decide what might become his or her favorite memory from the journey to America. Briefly describe the memory in the space provided below.

A Favorite Memory

Yonkel

Rifke

Chanah

Benjamin

Yaacov

Schmuel

Raizel

Pitsel

PLUS Activity

An Immigrant's Journal

Based on what you have learned from *The Cat Who Escaped from Steerage* and the PLUS pages, write several short journal entries as if you were an immigrant keeping a record of your experiences. You will be writing in the first person, using the pronouns *I, my, we,* and *our.*

You could begin your entries a day or two before your ship lands at Ellis Island; you could begin it with what happens to you and your family at Ellis Island; or you could have the journal start with your arrival in New York City. Each journal entry should be no longer than one page.

 The Cat Who Escaped from Steerage

Home Activity

Looking into Family History

Ask someone at home where your ancestors came from. Does anyone in your family know how or when they traveled to America? or about why they came in the first place? See what you can learn, and take notes so you can share information with your classmates.

Song of the Trees
by Mildred Taylor
illustrated by Jerry Pinkney

About the Book

During the Depression years, a black Mississippi landowner leaves his family to find work in Louisiana. While he is away, a neighboring white farmer begins to cut down ancient oak trees on his family's land. The family must face injustice and prejudice with dignity and determination.

Social Studies Links

This realistic fiction gives students an introduction to the kind of hateful attitudes and injustices that caused African Americans and people of conscience to support the Civil Rights movement. Students will empathize with the African American family in this story and will better understand the motives and actions of important reformers like Dr. Martin Luther King, Jr.

Getting Students Started

Read the author's frontispiece note aloud to the class. Remind students that when the Civil War and the Emancipation Proclamation ended slavery, they did not end the way some people regarded African Americans. By focusing on the key ideas of human dignity, personal integrity, and equal justice, this story helps students understand why civil rights for all Americans has been a significant social issue in the twentieth century. Assign the book for independent reading.

PLUS and Beyond

The Great Depression was a time of hardship for people in both urban and rural America. You may wish to have students read the PLUS pages before they read *Song of the Trees*. The background information will make the economic pressures on the characters more understandable.

Name _____ Date _____

  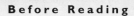

Song of the Trees

What is Injustice?

Justice—fair treatment—is something that every person is entitled to. People sometimes become angry if they feel that they are being treated unjustly.

Look through some recent newspapers or magazines, or think about recent news programs you have seen, to choose a situation in the news where a person or a group of people was not treated justly. It could be something that happened in this country or in some other part of the world.

Then answer the questions below in complete sentences.

1. **What was the situation, and what was unjust about it?**

   _____

   _____

2. **Describe the way you think the people in the situation felt about the injustice.**

   _____

   _____

3. **Could the situation have been avoided? How?**

   _____

   _____

4. **If you could have changed the situation to make it more just, would it have been just for others, too? Explain.**

   _____

   _____

As you read Song of the Trees, think about this idea of justice and fairness.

Name _____ Date _____

Reading Beyond the Words

1. Mr. Anderson offered money to **Big Ma** for the trees he wanted to cut, and she agreed. What was unfair about his offer and the way he made it?

   _____

   _____

   _____

2. After Mr. Anderson began to cut down trees, **Big Ma** and **Mama** sent **Stacey** to bring **Papa** home. If they thought the agreement with Mr. Anderson was unjust, why didn't they go talk to the local sheriff instead?

   _____

   _____

   _____

3. What makes Mr. Anderson think he can cut down all the trees he wants to?

   _____

   _____

   _____

4. Think about the events near the end of the story and about what **Papa** threatens to do. Why do you think **Papa** felt so strongly about stopping Mr. Anderson?

   _____

   _____

   _____

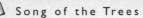
PLUS Activity

The Changing Value of Money

At the time of the Depression, one dollar would buy more than one dollar buys today. A rise in prices that causes money to become less valuable is called *inflation*.

Mr. Anderson offered Big Ma $65 for her trees. Today $65 does not seem like very much money, but during the 1930s, each dollar was worth more than it is today. Do some library research to learn how much $65 in 1931 would equal today. Then choose five products—one gallon of milk, for example—and make a chart that lists the prices of things then compared to the prices of things today.

Home Activity

What Would Someone Else Do?

Tell the story of Song of the Trees to someone at home, right up to the point at which Papa comes home. Then ask the person listening what he or she would do in Papa's place.

Compare the answer you get with what Papa did. Was it a similar solution or different?